Welcome to the world

PAINTING

Use paints and paintbrushes to finish the pictures in this book.

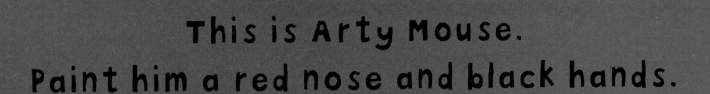

This is Arty Mouse.
Paint him a red nose and black hands.

Red, yellow and blue

The rainbow birds love red, yellow and blue. They use them to make other colours, too.

Clean your paintbrush in water before you use another colour.

red

Use the right colours to help the rainbow birds with their painting.

Summer meadow

Help Dot and Splat to fill the meadow
with yellow and blue flowers.

Dot

Mix blue
and yellow
paint here.

Scribble wants to make green.
Mix yellow and a tiny bit of blue
to help him.

Geo's purple wall

Geo is building a purple wall. Mix red and blue paint to make purple, so you can help.

Ask a grown-up to cut a small rectangle out of sponge. Dip it in the purple paint, then press it onto the page to make bricks.

Geo

You need lots of purple. This will be a big wall!

Dot's pots!

Dot has made two big pots.
Help her to decorate each one.

Dip your finger in black paint.
Use it to print a black dotty
pattern on the white pot.

Dip your finger in white paint.
Use it to print a white dotty
pattern on the black pot.

It looks like rain!

Uh-oh! Look at the big grey clouds!
Spiro thinks it's going to rain.

Spiro

Mix white and a tiny
bit of black to make
grey. Then paint
more clouds.

Mix more grey to paint the watering can and the puddle. Use a little more black to make a darker grey.

Pretty in pink!

Mix white and a little bit of red to make pink, then paint DOT's pretty bow.

Use lots of white and a tiny bit of red to make pale pink. Use more red for a darker pink.

Make Dot extra happy by painting a bunch of pink flowers.

Try adding white to other colours to make them lighter.

chocolate cakes

Scribble has made some cakes.
All they need is some
yummy chocolate icing!

Mix red, yellow and blue to make brown. Then paint chocolate icing on my cakes. Yum!

Messy Scribble!

Scribble looks messy after eating his cakes. Paint a brown chocolatey mouth and paws.

winter fun!

It's chilly playing in the snow.
Paint a colourful woolly hat for
each Arty friend.

stripy

Fill the sky with more white snowflakes to add to the winter fun!

What hat colours will you choose?

Arty's garden fence

Every year, Arty Mouse paints his garden fence to keep it white, bright and neat.

Paint the grey fence white to make it look like new.

Try to keep the paint inside the shapes. Be careful!

I'm painting my fence red. Please help ... try using a thin paintbrush!

Place your brush at the top.

Paint down and lift the brush off at the bottom.

Stripy's blankets

Stripy has knitted two cosy blankets — one for him and one for Dot.

Flying high!

Arty Mouse is flying high in the sky, but the sky needs painting!

Mix a pale blue colour. Then paint carefully around the fluffy white clouds to fill in the sky.

Splat attack!

Splat loves paint splats.
Help him to finish his
splatter painting.

Make lots of
different-coloured
splats!

Choose a colour and mix in water to make it runny. Dip the paintbrush in, hold it over Splat's paper and shake ... SPLAT!

This is messy! Use extra newspaper.

Furry friends

Scribble plays with his favourite teddy.
Can you add tufts of brown fur?

Paint your own furry toy
here. What will it be?

Spiro's spirals

Spiro is teaching Scribble how to make spiral shapes on the pond. Can you paint some too?

Put your paintbrush on the page and paint round and round, getting bigger as you go.

Start here

Today is sunny.
Can you paint a yellow
spiral sun in the sky?

Strawberry sundae

Stripy wants a strawberry sundae that goes from pale pink to dark pink.

Paint a strawberry on top!

Start with lots of white, then mix in a little red each time you paint a stripe.

Cosy campfire

The Arty friends are camping. Paint the flames on their campfire to keep them warm.

Start with lots of yellow for the bottom of the flames.

Work your way up the flames.

Mix a little red into your colour each time you paint a bit more.

Rock pool fun

Spiro has made some sea snail friends.

Paint each sea snail's shell a lighter
shade of its body colour.

Dot is collecting pebbles in pale colours. Can you help? Add some more pebbles on the beach.

It's raining!

Scribble likes the rain. Paint his boots red and paint his raincoat blue. Paint the puddles grey.

Paint carefully inside the shapes.

To print rain, mix lots of grey paint. Dip the edge of a card rectangle in the paint, then press it on the page.

Ask a grown-up to cut a small rectangle of card for you.

Dodgem cars

The Arty friends are at the funfair.
Paint their dodgem cars to match
the flags.

who is in the red, yellow and blue dodgems?

Fantastic fireworks

Mix pale colours so they show up in the dark sky.

Fireworks are great! Use any colours you like to paint lots of amazing sights for the Arty friends to see.

What will your fireworks look like?
Wiggly lines? Spirals? Dots?
Splats? You decide!

Pizza time

Hungry Geo is eating a huge pizza. What colours should the missing toppings be?

Can you spot the tomatoes, cheese and mushrooms?

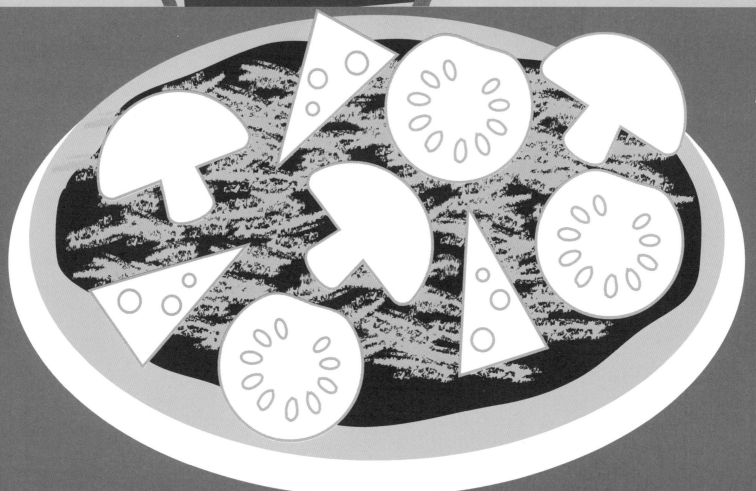

Fruity feast

Stripy chooses a healthy fruit salad. What colours should the missing fruits be?

Can you spot the strawberries, orange slices and grapes?

Arty air display

The Arty friends are flying their planes. Paint a coloured trail coming out of the back of each one.

Can you reach the right side before the paint runs out?

Whose trail will be the longest?

Dip your paintbrush in the paint, place it at the back of a plane and paint a trail as long as you can in one go.

Deep, blue sea

Splat and Stripy love sailing. Paint a sea of wavy lines from light blue near the surface to dark blue deep down.

Starlight, star bright

Scribble is studying
the night sky. Paint
lots of white stars and
colourful planets for
him to look at.

Use a thin
paintbrush to
paint faraway
stars.